John Hegar

C000070735

Mental Maths

T he first three Mental Maths books were all about the number bonds up to fifty, that is the basic facts such as **2 + 6 = 8**. This book revises the same number bonds to practise adding and taking away of numbers up to fifty, and then extends the work to include larger numbers up to one hundred. New ideas are usually presented in ways that point out the patterns in numbers, making links with what has already been learnt. For example, if you know that **2 + 6 = 8**, and that **32 + 6 = 38**, it should be easy to see that **62 + 6 = 68**, **92 + 6 = 98**, and so on.

    In this book multiplication is introduced for the first time. Your child will already have worked on multiplication at school, grouping real objects and working out sums on paper. Multiplying mentally is easy for the child who knows the tables. The old-fashioned way of reciting 'One two is two, two twos are four...' is still a good way of memorizing multiplication facts, or ask your child's teacher for some advice.

    Another idea in this book is that your child should start to check results without needing you or a teacher to do it. This helps to develop the confidence to work independently, and it will become more important later in Mental Maths.

Ages 9-10

Adding nine

38 + 9 = 47

27 + 9 = 36

39 + 9 = 48

42 + 9 = 51

33 + 9 = 42

35 + 9 = 44

14 + 9 = 23

36 + 9 = 45

41 + 9 = 50

37 + 9 = 46

Helper's tips

- Say 'Thirty-eight add nine makes ...'
- Remember the easy way to add nine: just add ten and take away one.

Adding eight

$$38 + 8 = 46$$

$$27 + 8 = 35$$

$$49 + 8 = 57$$

$$22 + 8 = 30$$

$$33 + 8 = 41$$

$$26 + 8 = 34$$

$$44 + 8 = 52$$

$$30 + 8 = 38$$

$$41 + 8 = 49$$

$$25 + 8 = 33$$

Helper's tip

Help your child to see the easy way of doing this: add ten and take away two.

Mixed adding

$$29 + 6 = 35$$

$$38 + 5 = 43$$

$$35 + 9 = 44$$

$$48 + 8 = 56$$

$$35 + 7 = 42$$

$$17 + 6 = 23$$

$$46 + 5 = 51$$

$$37 + 7 = 44$$

$$26 + 8 = 34$$

$$29 + 9 = 38$$

Helper's tips
- A short pause after the first number might help your child to visualize it.
- If your child has problems with this page use the previous book to practise the number bonds.

Mixed adding

$4 + 19 = 23$

$6 + 26 = 32$

$5 + 35 = 40$

$7 + 48 = 55$

$4 + 45 = 49$

$7 + 34 = 41$

$4 + 18 = 22$

$8 + 29 = 37$

$4 + 36 = 40$

$7 + 49 = 56$

Helper's tips
- Read each question twice if your child has difficulty.
- Make sure your child is not counting on fingers.

Take away ten

Take 10 from **43** = 33

Take 10 from **38** = 28

Take 10 from **24** = 14

Take 10 from **50** = 40

Take 10 from **27** = 17

Take 10 from **46** = 36

Take 10 from **32** = 22

Take 10 from **49** = 39

Take 10 from **35** = 25

Take 10 from **41** = 31

Helper's tips
- Read each question as it is written. This will help your child to focus on the number ten in each question.
- Your child should understand that this just involves taking one from the figure in the tens column.

Take away nine

Take 9 from 36 = 27

Take 9 from 44 = 35

Take 9 from 28 = 19

Take 9 from 42 = 33

Take 9 from 27 = 18

Take 9 from 49 = 40

Take 9 from 35 = 26

Take 9 from 43 = 34

Take 9 from 41 = 32

Take 9 from 30 = 21

Helper's tip

An easy way to do this is to take away ten then add one.

Take away eight

Take 8 from 38 = 30

Take 8 from 47 = 39

Take 8 from 29 = 21

Take 8 from 42 = 34

Take 8 from 33 = 25

Take 8 from 46 = 38

Take 8 from 24 = 16

Take 8 from 50 = 42

Take 8 from 41 = 33

Take 8 from 34 = 26

Helper's tip

Following the pattern of the previous page, can your child suggest an easy way to do this?

Mixed take-away

Take 4 from 36 = 32

Take 3 from 50 = 47

Take 5 from 36 = 31

Take 7 from 25 = 18

Take 4 from 41 = 37

Take 7 from 39 = 32

Take 3 from 41 = 38

Take 6 from 45 = 39

Take 7 from 44 = 37

Take 5 from 28 = 23

Helper's tip

Your child could work these out by adding on. For example, the first question becomes 'How many from 4 to 36?' From 4 to 10 is 6; from 10 to 36 is 26; 6 and 26 makes 32 added on altogether.

Mixed take-away

Take 7 from 36 = 29

Take 6 from 44 = 38

Take 3 from 43 = 40

Take 4 from 22 = 18

Take 5 from 34 = 29

Take 4 from 40 = 36

Take 6 from 31 = 25

Take 5 from 50 = 45

Take 3 from 46 = 43

Take 7 from 18 = 11

Helper's tip

Say 'How many from 7 to 36?' See the example on the previous page.

Change from 50 pence

50 pence – 23 pence = 27 pence

50 pence – 35 pence = 15 pence

50 pence – 38 pence = 12 pence

50 pence – 21 pence = 29 pence

50 pence – 34 pence = 16 pence

50 pence – 42 pence = 8 pence

50 pence – 17 pence = 33 pence

50 pence – 39 pence = 11 pence

50 pence – 10 pence = 40 pence

50 pence – 46 pence = 4 pence

Helper's tip

This can be turned into an adding task by adding on to get to the next ten, then adding tens as necessary to get to fifty. See the example on page 9.

Adding tens

$$30 + 30 = 60$$

$$50 + 20 = 70$$

$$30 + 60 = 90$$

$$20 + 50 = 70$$

$$40 + 20 = 60$$

$$10 + 30 = 40$$

$$40 + 30 = 70$$

$$20 + 40 = 60$$

$$50 + 10 = 60$$

$$20 + 70 = 90$$

Helper's tip

Say 'Thirty add thirty ...'. Thirty means three tens, so it's just 3 (tens) + 3 (tens) = 6 (tens). Your child should recognize these familiar number bonds.

Adding tens

$26 + 10 = 36$

$42 + 20 = 62$

$20 + 33 = 53$

$13 + 50 = 63$

$24 + 20 = 44$

$20 + 45 = 65$

$16 + 60 = 76$

$30 + 27 = 57$

$58 + 20 = 78$

$70 + 19 = 89$

Helper's tip

This time one of the numbers has a units figure, but your child should see that the units figure stays the same and only the tens figure changes.

Adding nineteen

16 + 19 = 35

24 + 19 = 43

18 + 19 = 37

22 + 19 = 41

17 + 19 = 36

19 + 19 = 38

25 + 19 = 44

13 + 19 = 32

21 + 19 = 40

30 + 19 = 49

Helper's tip

A good way of adding nineteen is to add twenty and take away one. Suggest this to your child before you begin this page.

Adding nineteen

$$28 + 19 = 47$$

$$17 + 19 = 36$$

$$39 + 19 = 58$$

$$42 + 19 = 61$$

$$23 + 19 = 42$$

$$36 + 19 = 55$$

$$54 + 19 = 73$$

$$40 + 19 = 59$$

$$61 + 19 = 80$$

$$34 + 19 = 53$$

Helper's tip
Does it make any difference if you take away one first, and then add twenty?

Three and two

$$3 + 2 = 5$$

$$13 + 2 = 15$$

$$23 + 2 = 25$$

$$33 + 2 = 35$$

$$13 + 12 = 25$$

$$13 + 22 = 35$$

$$33 + 22 = 55$$

$$23 + 32 = 55$$

$$43 + 22 = 65$$

$$83 + 12 = 95$$

Helper's tips

- We are adding both tens and units for the first time, but the units always use the same number bond, so your child can concentrate on the tens.
- Make sure your child notices that 3 + 2 is always 5, no matter what other figures come in front.

Six and seven

$$6 + 7 = 13$$

$$16 + 7 = 23$$

$$26 + 7 = 33$$

$$36 + 7 = 43$$

$$46 + 7 = 53$$

$$6 + 17 = 23$$

$$16 + 17 = 33$$

$$26 + 17 = 43$$

$$26 + 27 = 53$$

$$36 + 37 = 73$$

Helper's tips

- Again these questions all use the same number bond. Noticing this kind of pattern makes maths much easier.
- Use a calculator to add a five-figure number ending in 6 to a five-figure number ending in 7. What will the result end in?

Eight and four

$$8 + 4 = 12$$

$$18 + 4 = 22$$

$$28 + 4 = 32$$

$$18 + 14 = 32$$

$$28 + 14 = 42$$

$$28 + 24 = 52$$

$$24 + 38 = 62$$

$$34 + 38 = 72$$

$$48 + 14 = 62$$

$$64 + 18 = 82$$

Helper's tips

- For extra practice change the numbers so that they end in 9 and 3 instead of 8 and 4. How will that change the results?
- Ask your child how to tell which of the following is correct (without using a calculator): 2538 + 4974 = 7635 or 7512 or 7406. (It must be the one that ends in 2.)

Mixed adding

$$27 + 13 = 40$$

$$45 + 25 = 70$$

$$36 + 24 = 60$$

$$52 + 18 = 70$$

$$19 + 31 = 50$$

$$25 + 14 = 39$$

$$45 + 13 = 58$$

$$22 + 15 = 37$$

$$81 + 16 = 97$$

$$54 + 12 = 66$$

Helper's tips

- Your child should choose whether to add the tens first or the units first.
- The first five questions are easier: they use the bonds that make ten.

Mixed adding

$23 + 36 = 59$

$41 + 17 = 58$

$68 + 11 = 79$

$24 + 23 = 47$

$34 + 51 = 85$

$65 + 16 = 81$

$48 + 14 = 62$

$28 + 17 = 45$

$66 + 18 = 84$

$48 + 19 = 67$

Helper's tip

In the second group of questions the units figures add up to more than ten. Your child should work them out in three stages. For example, one way of doing this is: $5 + 6 = 11$; $60 + 10 = 70$; $70 + 11 = 81$.

Mixed adding

$$12 + 49 = 61$$

$$19 + 24 = 43$$

$$16 + 27 = 43$$

$$17 + 45 = 62$$

$$18 + 33 = 51$$

$$17 + 47 = 64$$

$$16 + 32 = 48$$

$$17 + 49 = 66$$

$$19 + 26 = 45$$

$$18 + 28 = 46$$

Helper's tip

Your child might need to hear each question twice.

Mixed adding

23 + 19 = 42

18 + 25 = 43

47 + 14 = 61

54 + 14 = 68

29 + 39 = 68

36 + 46 = 82

25 + 19 = 44

63 + 23 = 86

47 + 12 = 59

41 + 55 = 96

Helper's tips

- With these larger numbers, if your child has problems adding tens and units mentally, copy the questions on to paper so that the number bonds can be seen.
- Revise any number bonds that your child is unsure of.

Multiplying by two

$6 \times 2 = 12$

$4 \times 2 = 8$

$5 \times 2 = 10$

$9 \times 2 = 18$

$2 \times 2 = 4$

$7 \times 2 = 14$

$3 \times 2 = 6$

$10 \times 2 = 20$

$1 \times 2 = 2$

$8 \times 2 = 16$

Helper's tips
- Say 'six twos are ...'
- Ask your child to recite the two times table: 'One two is two; two twos are four ...'

Multiplying by ten

$$6 \times 10 = 60$$

$$4 \times 10 = 40$$

$$5 \times 10 = 50$$

$$9 \times 10 = 90$$

$$2 \times 10 = 20$$

$$7 \times 10 = 70$$

$$3 \times 10 = 30$$

$$10 \times 10 = 100$$

$$1 \times 10 = 10$$

$$8 \times 10 = 80$$

Helper's tip

Ten is the easiest table because of the way our number system works. Try making a multiplication table with Roman numerals!

Multiplying by five

$6 \times 5 = 30$

$4 \times 5 = 20$

$5 \times 5 = 25$

$9 \times 5 = 45$

$2 \times 5 = 10$

$7 \times 5 = 35$

$3 \times 5 = 15$

$10 \times 5 = 50$

$1 \times 5 = 5$

$8 \times 5 = 40$

Helper's tips

- Help your child to look for patterns: odd numbers of fives end in five, even numbers of fives end in zero.
- Five is half of ten, so you can multiply by ten and halve the result.

Multiplying by four

6 × 4 = 24

4 × 4 = 16

5 × 4 = 20

9 × 4 = 36

2 × 4 = 8

7 × 4 = 28

3 × 4 = 12

10 × 4 = 40

1 × 4 = 4

8 × 4 = 32

Helper's tips

- Your child needs to memorize the tables, but noticing patterns can make the learning easier. Compare the four times table with the two times table.
- Use dice to practise tables: whatever number you throw, multiply it by four.

Multiplying by three

$$6 \times 3 = 18$$

$$4 \times 3 = 12$$

$$5 \times 3 = 15$$

$$9 \times 3 = 27$$

$$2 \times 3 = 6$$

$$7 \times 3 = 21$$

$$3 \times 3 = 9$$

$$10 \times 3 = 30$$

$$1 \times 3 = 3$$

$$8 \times 3 = 24$$

Helper's tip

From 1×1 up to 10×10 there are 100 multiplying facts
that your child needs to know. We have now used
more than half of them. Revise any of these tables that
your child is unsure of.

Mixed multiplying

$$4 \times 3 = 12$$

$$3 \times 4 = 12$$

$$8 \times 3 = 24$$

$$6 \times 10 = 60$$

$$9 \times 4 = 36$$

$$7 \times 2 = 14$$

$$6 \times 5 = 30$$

$$9 \times 2 = 18$$

$$3 \times 10 = 30$$

$$2 \times 4 = 8$$

Helper's tip

'Four threes' is a different fact from 'three fours' but the result is the same. In effect, this halves the number of facts that need to be learnt. Can your child think of other pairs of results?

Mixed multiplying

$9 \times 3 = 27$

$8 \times 10 = 80$

$7 \times 4 = 28$

$5 \times 2 = 10$

$4 \times 5 = 20$

$7 \times 3 = 21$

$6 \times 4 = 24$

$2 \times 10 = 20$

$9 \times 5 = 45$

$3 \times 2 = 6$

Helper's tip

These five pages of mixed multiplying practise every one of the facts in the two, three, four, five and ten times tables. Go back to the tables if your child needs more practice.

Mixed multiplying

$5 \times 4 = 20$

$6 \times 3 = 18$

$7 \times 10 = 70$

$8 \times 5 = 40$

$4 \times 2 = 8$

$10 \times 3 = 30$

$7 \times 5 = 35$

$4 \times 10 = 40$

$1 \times 2 = 2$

$4 \times 4 = 16$

Helper's tip

Your child should have noticed that the order of the numbers doesn't matter in multiplying. You can draw attention to this by reversing all these questions: 4×5, 3×6, and so on.